THE ROYAL HORTICULTURAL SOCIETY ADDRESS BOOK

Early paintings and drawings of fruit and flowers

Commentary by Brent Elliott

FRANCES LINCOLN

Frances Lincoln Limited
4 Torriano Mews
Torriano Avenue
London NW5 2RZ

British Library cataloguing-in-publication data
A catalogue record for this book is available from the British Library.

ISBN 0-7112-1069-1

Typeset by Clive Dorman & Co.
Printed in Hong Kong

First Frances Lincoln edition: July 1996

FRONT COVER
A hand-coloured engraving after Georg Dionysius Ehret (1708-1770), from his book Plantae ac papiliones rariores depictae *(1748-59), depicting* Coreopsis verticillata, Gloxinia maculata, *and the Guernsey lily,* Nerine sarniensis

TITLE PAGE
A watercolour drawing of a cyclamen by Pieter van Holsteyn (c.1614-1673)

OPPOSITE
A hand-coloured engraving by Pierre-Joseph Redouté (1759-1840) of a waterlily, Nymphaea caerulea, *from Etienne-Pierre Ventenat's* Jardin de la Malmaison *(1803-1805)*

BACK COVER
A watercolour drawing of an iris, labelled 'Iris flambé', from the Flore du désert, *an anonymous collection of French drawings of the first decade of the nineteenth century*

A NAME	ADDRESS	TEL & FAX

*A hand-coloured engraving of the so-called 'German apricot', from
Giorgio Gallesio's* Pomona italiana *(1817-1839), after a drawing
by Antonio Serantoni (*fl. *1810s-1840s)*

NAME ADDRESS TEL & FAX

A hand-coloured engraving after Georg Dionysius Ehret (1708-1770), from his book Plantae ac papiliones rariores depictae *(1748-1759), depicting Indian hemp,* (Hibiscus cannabinus), Iris versicolor, *and* Mollugo verticillata

ADDRESS TEL & FAX

A watercolour drawing of a hyacinth by Pieter van Holsteyn (c. 1614-1673)

NAME	ADDRESS	TEL & FAX

A watercolour drawing of strawberry 'Wilmot's Superb', made in 1824 for the Horticultural Society by Charles John Robertson

NAME

ADDRESS

TEL & FAX

*A drawing in oil on paper of tulip cultivars, from an unpublished florilegium by
Pieter van Kouwenhoorn (fl. 1620s-1630s)*

C NAME | ADDRESS | TEL & FAX

C NAME ADDRESS TEL & FAX

C NAME	ADDRESS	TEL & FAX

A watercolour drawing of Iris sordida *(now included in* Iris spuria)*,
drawn in 1825 by John Curtis (1791-1862)*

D

D NAME	ADDRESS	TEL & FAX

A hand-coloured engraving of pear 'Poire de Vallée', from Duhamel du Monceau's
Traité des arbres fruitiers *(1807-1835), after a drawing*
by Pierre-Antoine Poiteau (1766-1854)

D **NAME** **ADDRESS** **TEL** *&* **FAX**

D NAME	ADDRESS	TEL & FAX

NAME   **ADDRESS**   **TEL & FAX**

A hand-coloured engraving by Pierre-Joseph Redouté (1759-1840) of Magnolia hypoleuca, from Etienne-Pierre Ventenat's Jardin de la Malmaison (1830-1835)

NAME	ADDRESS	TEL & FAX

A hand-coloured engraving of a Georgian almond, from Duhamel du Monceau's
Traité des arbres fruitiers *(1807-1835), after a drawing by*
Pierre-Jean-François Turpin (1775-1840)

F   NAME   ADDRESS   TEL & FAX

*A watercolour drawing of the 'Damson' grape, made for the Horticultural Society
in 1817 by William Hooker (1779-1832)*

F'

NAME	ADDRESS	TEL & FAX

A watercolour drawing of a fritillary, a guelder-rose, plums, raspberries and butterflies by P. van Weinsel, an undocumented artist of the eighteenth century

F	NAME	ADDRESS	TEL & FAX

F NAME	ADDRESS	TEL & FAX

G	NAME	ADDRESS	TEL & FAX

A watercolour drawing of Rosa foetida *'Bicolor' by*
Emma or Emmeline Smith (fl. *1780s*)

A watercolour drawing of apple 'Lucombe's Seedling', drawn for the
Horticultural Society in 1821 by Charles John Robertson

NAME   ADDRESS   TEL & FAX

H	NAME	ADDRESS	TEL & FAX

*A hand-coloured engraving by Georg Dionysius Ehret (1708-1770) of the
Turkscap lily,* Lilium superbum, *from C.J. Trew's* Plantae selectae *(1750-1765)*

H

NAME	ADDRESS	TEL & FAX

A hand-coloured engraving from Jean-Louis Prévost's Collection des fleurs
et des fruits *(1805), depicting the giant sunflower,* Helianthus annuus

NAME	ADDRESS	TEL & FAX

H NAME   ADDRESS   TEL & FAX

A hand-coloured engraving from Jean Louis Prévost's Collection des fleurs
et des fruits *(1805), depicting two varieties of grape ('Chasselas Blanc',
'Muscat Rouge'), peach 'Pouprée Hative', and plum 'Damas d'Italie'*

NAME ADDRESS TEL *&* FAX

*A drawing in oil on paper of species and varieties of daffodil, from an
unpublished florilegium by Pieter van Kouwenhoorn* (fl. *1620s-1630s*)

A watercolour drawing of Amaryllis belladonna (Hippeastrum equestre*),
by Pierre Ledoulx (1730-1807), from an album of plants growing in the garden
of J. van Huerna, near Bruges, between 1792 and 1815*

NAME   ADDRESS   TEL & FAX

A hand-coloured engraving of cherry 'Gros Bigarreau Rouge', from
Duhamel du Monceau's Traité des arbres fruitiers (1807-1835), after a
drawing by Pierre-Antoine Poiteau (1766-1854)

K NAME	ADDRESS	TEL & FAX

A hand-coloured engraving from Jean-Louis Prévost's Collection des fleurs et
des fruits *(1805), depicting* Iris pallida, Rosa centifolia *and* Narcissus *'Soleil d'Or'*

K

K	NAME	ADDRESS	TEL & FAX

A watercolour drawing of an iberis by Pieter van Holsteyn (c. 1614-1673)

A watercolour drawing of varieties of oranges and lemons, by Pierre Ledoulx
(1730-1807), from an album of plants growing in the garden of J. van Huerna,
near Bruges, between 1792 and 1815

L NAME	ADDRESS	TEL & FAX

A watercolour drawing of Lantana camara *by Eliza or Elizabeth Smith* (fl. 1780s)

L NAME	ADDRESS	TEL & FAX

L NAME	ADDRESS	TEL & FAX

M	NAME	ADDRESS	TEL & FAX

A watercolour drawing of auricula 'Wood's Delight'
by Sydenham Teast Edwards (1768-1819)

M

M	NAME	ADDRESS	TEL & FAX

A hand-coloured engraving of fig 'Brogiotto nero' from Giorgio Gallesio's
Pomona italiana *(1817-1839), after a drawing by Giuseppe Bucherelli (fl. 1820s-1840s)*

M	NAME	ADDRESS	TEL & FAX

M	NAME	ADDRESS	TEL & FAX

N	NAME	ADDRESS	TEL & FAX

A watercolour drawing by Sydenham Teast Edwards (1768-1819) of a crabapple, Malus coronaria, *the original drawing for plate 2009 of* Curtis's Botanical Magazine, *published in 1818*

N	NAME	ADDRESS	TEL & FAX

A watercolour drawing by Pancrace Bessa (1772-1830), of Robinia viscosa,
made for the Herbier général de l'amateur

N	NAME	ADDRESS	TEL & FAX

A watercolour of a pineapple, drawn for the Horticultural Society in 1817
by William Hooker (1779-1832)

O

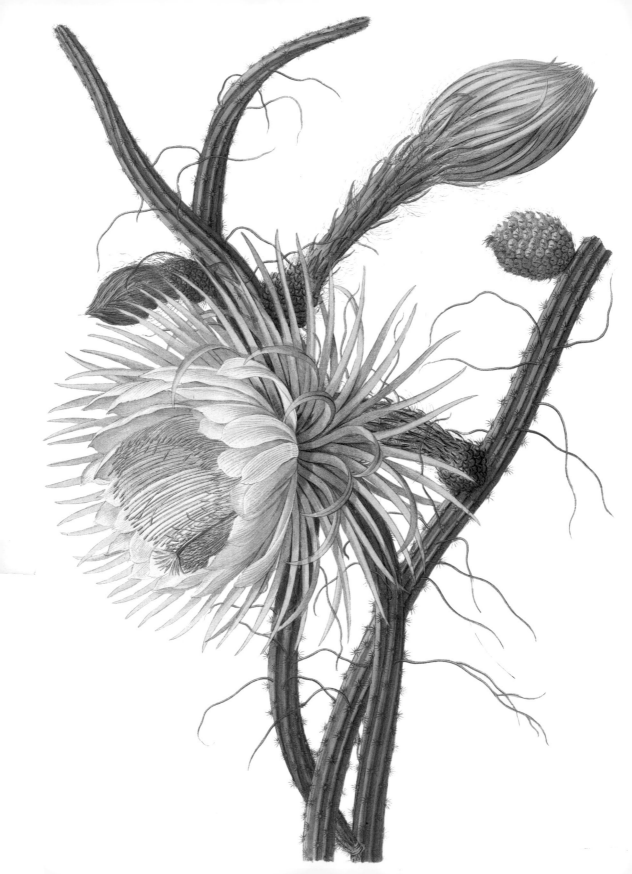

NAME ADDRESS TEL & FAX

---

*A hand-coloured engraving by Georg Dionysius Ehret (1708-1770) of
cactus Queen-of-the-Night, Selenicereus grandiflorus, from C.J. Trew's
Plantae selectae (1750-1765)*

NAME ADDRESS TEL & FAX

A coloured drawing in oil on vellum of the coral plant, Jatropha multifida,
by Claude Aubriet (1665-1742)

P
Q

*A watercolour drawing of peach 'Titon de Virnes', drawn for the
Horticultural Society in 1822 by Barbara Cotton* (fl. 1820s)

PQ	NAME	ADDRESS	TEL & FAX

A watercolour drawing of a foxglove, Digitalis purpurea, *by Ferdinand Bauer (1760-1826), made for John Lindley's* Digitalium monographia *(1821)*

R

R	NAME	ADDRESS	TEL & FAX

A watercolour drawing of a double form of Clematis viticella
by Margaret Meen (d. 1824)

R NAME	ADDRESS	TEL & FAX

A hand-coloured engraving of plum 'Damas d'Espagne' from Duhamel du Monceau's Traité des arbres fruitiers *(1807-1835), after a drawing by Pierre-Jean-François Turpin (1775-1840)*

S

S	NAME	ADDRESS	TEL & FAX

A hand-coloured engraving from Jean-Louis Prévost's Collection des fleurs et des fruits *(1805), depicting three cultivars of the opium poppy,* Papaver somnifera

S NAME	ADDRESS	TEL & FAX

S	NAME	ADDRESS	TEL & FAX

S NAME	ADDRESS	TEL & FAX

A hand-coloured engraving of a bizarre tulip, 'Peregrinus Apostolicus', from
The Florist's Delight *(1789-1791) by James Sowerby (1757-1822)*

T

T NAME	ADDRESS	TEL & FAX

A hand-coloured engraving of pear 'Angelica', from Giorgio Gallesio's
Pomona italiana *(1817-1839), after a drawing by Isabella Bozzolini* (fl. 1820s-1840s)

T	NAME	ADDRESS	TEL & FAX

An unsigned hand-coloured engraving of Sphaeralcea abutiloides, *from the*
Plantarum rariorum Horti Caesarii Schoenbrunnensis descriptiones et icones
(1797-1804) by Nicolas Freiherr von Jacquin (1727-1817)

U
V

UV NAME	ADDRESS	TEL & FAX

*A watercolour by Sydenham Teast Edwards (1768-1819) of the original drawing
for plate 1665 of Curtis's* Botanical Magazine, *published in 1814 as*
Gladiolus blandus, *although the identification is uncertain*

NAME   ADDRESS   TEL & FAX

A hand-coloured engraving of pear 'Grosse roussette d'Anjou' from
Duhamel du Monceau's Traité des arbres fruitiers *(1807-1835), after a*
drawing by Pierre-Antoine Poiteau (1766-1854)

NAME   ADDRESS   TEL *&* FAX

A hand-coloured engraving from Jean-Louis Prévost's Collection des fleurs
et des fruits *(1805), depicting a tree mallow,* Lavatera trimestris,
and a white form of Nerium oleander

W NAME   ADDRESS   TEL & FAX

W	NAME	ADDRESS	TEL & FAX

XYZ NAME	ADDRESS	TEL *&* FAX

A hand-coloured engraving from Jean-Louis Prévost's Collection des fleurs et des fruits *(1805), depicting periwinkle* (Vinca rosea), Phlox divaricata, *and a garden form of cornflower* (Centaurea cyanus)

X
Y
Z

XYZ NAME	ADDRESS	TEL & FAX

A watercolour drawing of Delphinium elatum *by Margaret Meen (d. 1824)*

BIOGRAPHIES

AUBRIET, CLAUDE (1665-1742), *while working in Paris, attracted the attention of the great botanist Tournefort, who commissioned him to produce illustrations for his* Institutiones rei herbariae *(1700). From 1700 to 1702 Aubriet and Tournefort travelled together in the Near East. Aubriet went on to become the official artist of the Jardin des Plantes, a position he held until his death in 1742. The genus* Aubretia *was named in his honour.*

BAUER, FERDINAND (1760-1826) *began his career at the Vienna Botanic Garden in the 1780s, where he was employed by Jacquin to illustrate his* Icones plantarum rariorum. *In 1784 he accompanied the English botanist John Sibthorp to Greece, and subsequently drew the illustrations for Sibthorp's posthumous* Flora Graeca. *From 1801 to 1805 he was a botanical artist on Matthew Flinders' expedition to Australia; Flinders named Cape Bauer in his honour. Some of his drawings from this expedition were published in 1813 as* Illustrationes florae Novae Hollandiae, *though most remained unpublished until 1976. Among his other works were the plates for Lambert's* Genus Pinus. *His brother Franz (1758-1840), also a botanical artist, was associated with Kew Gardens and Sir Joseph Banks.*

BESSA, PANCRACE (1772-1830) *was a pupil of Spaendonck and Redouté. Between 1810 and 1827, he produced 527 illustrations for a work entitled* Herbier général de l'amateur, *one of the most popular French illustrated works on garden plants, which exists in two editions with different texts. The drawings for this work were given by Charles X to the Duchesse de Berry, to whom Bessa had given painting lessons; she in turn left them to her sister, the Empress of Brazil, and in 1947 the collection was finally dispersed at auction. A few of the drawings are now in the Lindley Library.*

BOZZOLINI, ISABELLA *and* BUCHERELLI, GIUSEPPE (fl. *1820s-1840s) were Italian artists, known primarily as illustrators of Giorgio Gallesio's* Pomona italiana *(1817-1839), the greatest Italian fruit book.*

COTTON, BARBARA (fl. *1820s), the third of the Horticultural Society's painters, was hired in 1822. Little is known of her career outside the Society; she lived in Newport Pagnell and exhibited at the Royal Academy between 1815 and 1822.*

CURTIS, JOHN (1791-1862), *born in Norwich, worked as an engraver for the Horticultural Society's* Transactions *before becoming the principal artist for the* Botanical Magazine, *for which he made over 400 illustrations by 1832. He is remembered primarily as an entomologist, although his multi-volume* British Entomology *(1824-1839) includes illustrations of plants as well as insects.*

EDWARDS, SYDENHAM TEAST (1768-1819), *trained as an artist by William Curtis, made most of the illustrations for Curtis's* Botanical Magazine *from 1787 until 1815, when he resigned to found his own rival publication, the* Botanical Register, *which was later edited by John Lindley.*

EHRET, GEORG DIONYSIUS (1708-1770) *was apprenticed in the garden of the Margrave of Baden at Karlsruhe. In 1736 he began drawing plant portraits for George Clifford of*

Hartecamp, which were used in Linnaeus's Hortus Cliffortianus. *Shortly thereafter he moved to England, where he spent the rest of his career working at the Chelsea Physic Garden, the Oxford Botanic Garden, and for patrons such as the 3rd Earl of Bute and the Duchess of Portland, though he kept a working relationship with Christoph Jakob Trew (1695-1769), with whom he collaborated on several volumes. By the time of his death in 1770 he was widely regarded as the best botanical artist of his day.*

HOLSTEYN, PIETER VAN *(c. 1614-1673) spent his life in Haarlem and became a Guild member there. There is little documentation of his career; as a flower painter he is mainly known for a volume of drawings now in the Lindley Library.*

HOOKER, WILLIAM *(1779-1832) was a pupil of Franz Bauer. His first important commission was the plates for R.A. Salisbury's* Paradisus Londinensis *(1805-1808); Salisbury was a founder member of the Horticultural Society, which hired Hooker in 1815 as its first artist. He is best known for the fruit drawings he made for the society and for his* Pomona Londinensis. *In 1822, however, he stopped painting, probably as the result of a stroke. He is commemorated in the colour name 'Hooker green'.*

JACQUIN, NICOLAS FREIHERR VON *(1727-1817), an Austrian botanist, was Director of the Vienna Botanic Garden. He published prolifically, issuing tome after tome describing the rare plants and new introductions in Vienna; for these works he employed a variety of artists, including the young Bauer brothers, but the plates in his books are not signed. Some of them may be his own work, for he was himself a good botanical artist.*

KOUWENHOORN, PIETER VAN *(fl. 1620s-1630s) was a glass painter working in Haarlem and Leiden where he was best known for his windows in the Annahofje. There also exists, however, an album of 46 coloured drawings on paper, bound in vellum, with a manuscript title page inscribed 'Verzameling van bloemen naar de natuur geteekend door (Collection of flowers drawn from nature by) Pieter van Kouwenhoorn', now in the Lindley Library. This work was obviously prepared with publication in mind, but never published.*

LEDOULX, PIERRE *(1730-1807), a Belgian artist, is known as a plant illustrator because of a series of drawings, commissioned by J. van Huerna to depict the plants in his garden near Bruges. The series of drawings, which eventually came to include the work of three other artists as well, is today in the Lindley Library.*

MEEN, MARGARET *(d. 1824) exhibited at the Royal Academy from 1775 to 1805, and died in 1824. In 1790 she published two parts of a folio work,* Exotic Plants from the Royal Gardens at Kew.

POITEAU, PIERRE-ANTOINE *(1766-1854), a French horticulturist, artist and author of a* Flora Parisiensis *and the* Pomologie française, *also made illustrations for a wide variety of other people's books. He was particularly skilled at fruit illustration, and both edited and helped to illustrate the massive revised edition of Duhamel du Monceau's* Traité des arbres fruitiers, *published between 1807 and 1835.*

PREVOST, JEAN LOUIS *(c.1760-1810), a French artist, was best known in his day as a landscape painter. In 1805 he published a volume entitled* Collection des fleurs et des fruits, *intended to serve as patterns for tapestry and wallpaper makers and other decorators.*

REDOUTE, PIERRE-JOSEPH *(1759-1840). Beginning his career as an artist under the direction of botanists like Candolle and L'Héritier de Brutelle, Redouté developed a great reputation for the beauty and accuracy of his work, and attracted imperial patronage. His massive works* Les liliacées *(1802-1816) and* Les roses *(1817-1824) are his major achievement, but he followed these up with anthologies of illustrations such as* Choix des plus belles fleurs *(1827-1833).*

ROBERTSON, CHARLES JOHN *(fl. 1820s) was hired by the Horticultural Society in 1820 to succeed William Hooker on his retirement. Nothing is known about Robertson's life and career apart from the 28 drawings of fruits in the Hooker series, made between 1820 and 1825.*

SERANTONI, ANTONIO *(fl. 1810s -1840s), an Italian artist, was one of the illustrators of Giorgio Gallesio's* Pomona italiana *(1817-1839).*

SMITH, AUGUSTA, ELIZA *or* ELIZABETH, *and* EMMA *or* EMMELINE *(fl. 1780s) were three sisters (it is presumed), several of whose drawings are now in the Lindley Library. Attempts to identify them with known artists of those names in the late eighteenth and early nineteenth centuries have so far proved inconclusive. The drawings signed by Augusta Smith form a part of a series numbered as though intended for publication or at least as a bound volume in a private collection.*

SOWERBY, JAMES *(1757-1822) worked both as an engraver (e.g. for Sibthorp's* Flora Graeca*) and as a botanical artist. In addition to making several plates for the* Botanical Magazine, *he published a four-volume work of* Coloured figures of English fungi *(1795-1815), and illustrated two major publications for Sir James Edward Smith:* English Botany *(1790-1814), and* Exotic Botany *(1804-1805). The plates reproduced here are taken from* The Florists' Delight *(1789-1791), a volume depicting florists' flowers.*

TURPIN, PIERRE-JEAN-FRANÇOIS *(1775-1840) was one of the most important and prolific botanical artists of his time. Among the works which he illustrated were the 'Nouveau Duhamel' (*Traité des arbres fruitiers, *1807-1835),* Humboldt and Bonpland's Voyage aux régions equinoctiales, *and Chaumeton's* Flore médicale. *For this last work Turpin and his collaborator Poiret wrote a supplement entitled* Leçons de flore, *which was separately published in 1820; in this Turpin showed himself to be an original botanist as well as an artist.*

WEINSEL, P. VAN *The Lindley Library contains one drawing (reproduced here) by this eighteenth-century artist, about whom no biographical information has been discovered.*